THIRTEEN

REMY CHARLIP & JERRY JOYNER

PARENTS' MAGAZINE PRESS NEW YORK, NEW YORK

LIBRARY OF CONGRESS CATALOGING IN PUBLICATION DATA
CHARLIP, REMY.
THIRTEEN.
SUMMARY: THIRTEEN PICTURE STORIES
DEVELOP SEPARATELY AND SIMULTANEOUSLY.
I. JOYNER, JERRY, JOINT AUTHOR. II. TITLE.
PZ7.C3812TH [FIC] 75-8875
ISBN 0-8193-0807-2
ISBN 0-8193-0808-0 LIB. BDG.

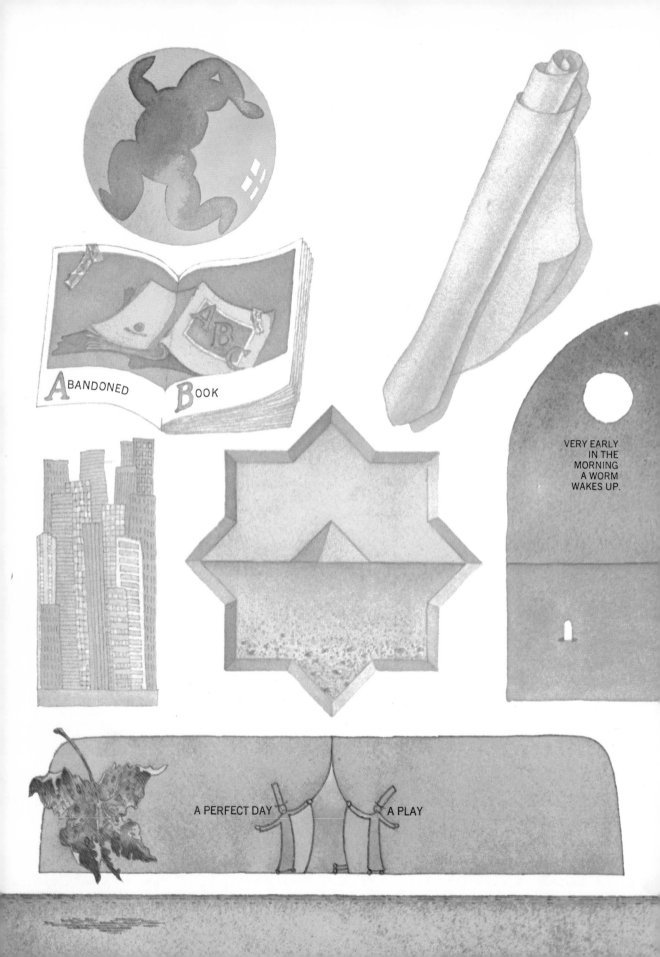

ABANDONED BOOK

VERY EARLY
IN THE
MORNING
A WORM
WAKES UP.

A PERFECT DAY   A PLAY

13

SWANS BECOMING WATER

VERY EARLY IN THE MORNING A WORM WAKES UP.

THIS IS A VERY OLD SHIP.

IT DOESN'T FIT

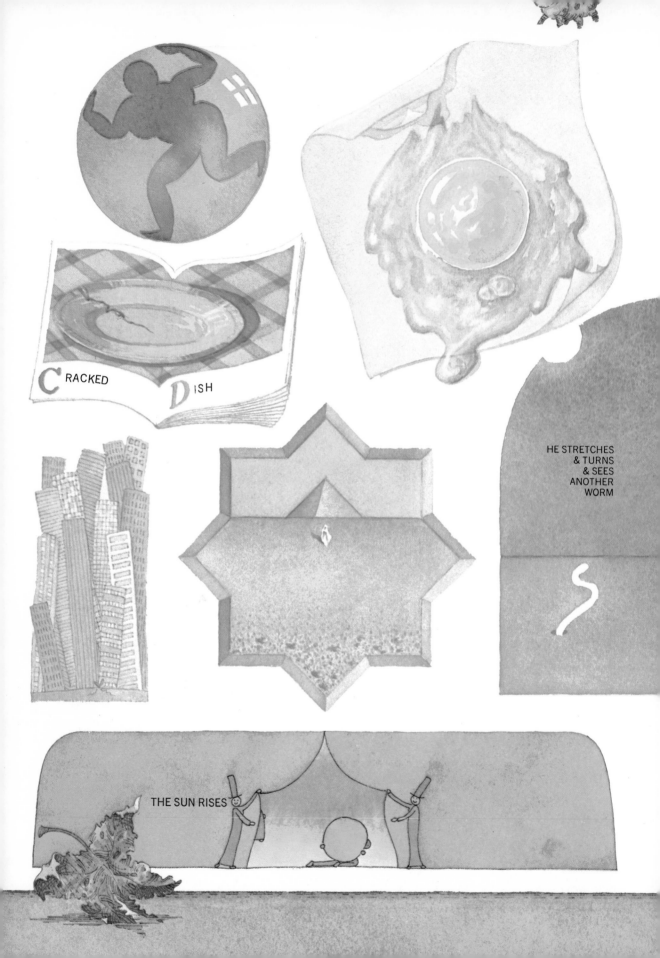

CRACKED DISH

HE STRETCHES
& TURNS
& SEES
ANOTHER
WORM

THE SUN RISES

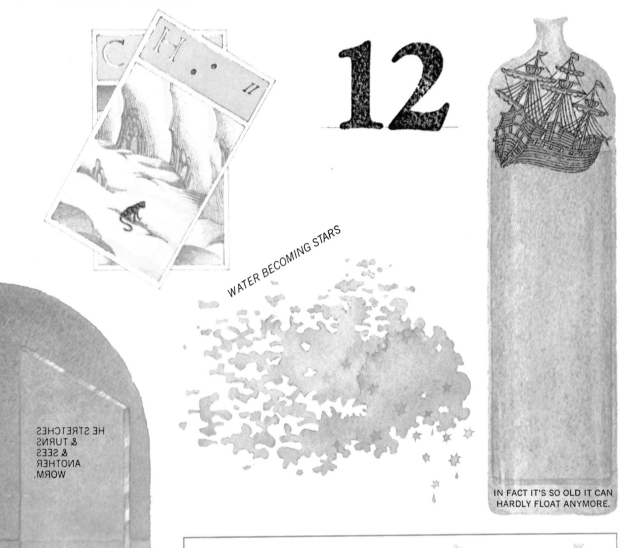

12

WATER BECOMING STARS

IN FACT IT'S SO OLD IT CAN
HARDLY FLOAT ANYMORE.

HE STRETCHES
& TURNS
& SEES
ANOTHER
WORM.

11

10

IT DOESN'T FIT

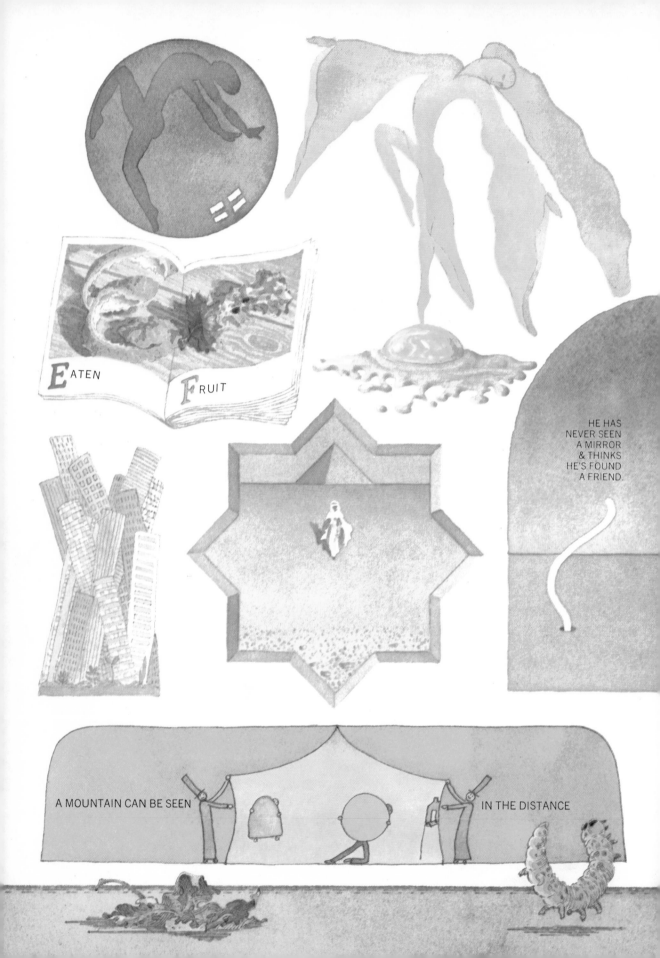

11

STARS BECOMING TREE

IN FACT IT'S SINKING.

HE HAS NEVER SEEN A MIRROR & THINKS HE'S FOUND A FRIEND.

IT DOESN'T FIT

10

9

GREASY HANDKERCHIEF

"HELLO,"
HE SAYS,
BUT THE
OTHER WORM
DOESN'T
ANSWER.

A VERY OLD HOUSE RESTS   ON TOP OF THE MOUNTAIN

10

CHAZM

TREE BECOMING LOBSTER

"HELLO," HE SAYS, BUT THE OTHER WORM DOESN'T ANSWER.

BUT IT DOESN'T MIND.

9

8

IT DOESN'T FIT

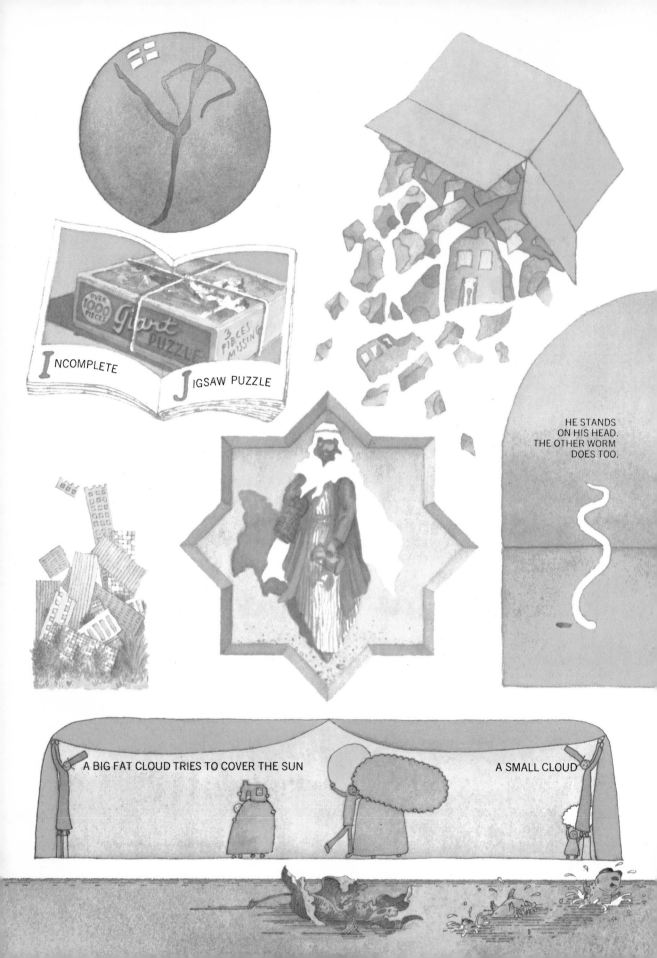

INCOMPLETE JIGSAW PUZZLE

3 PIECES MISSING

OVER 1000 PIECES

Giant PUZZLE

HE STANDS
ON HIS HEAD.
THE OTHER WORM
DOES TOO.

A BIG FAT CLOUD TRIES TO COVER THE SUN

A SMALL CLOUD

9

LOBSTER BECOMING ANGEL

HE STANDS
ON HIS HEAD.
THE OTHER WORM
DOES TOO.

IT'S BEEN EVERYWHERE.

8

7

IT DOESN'T FIT

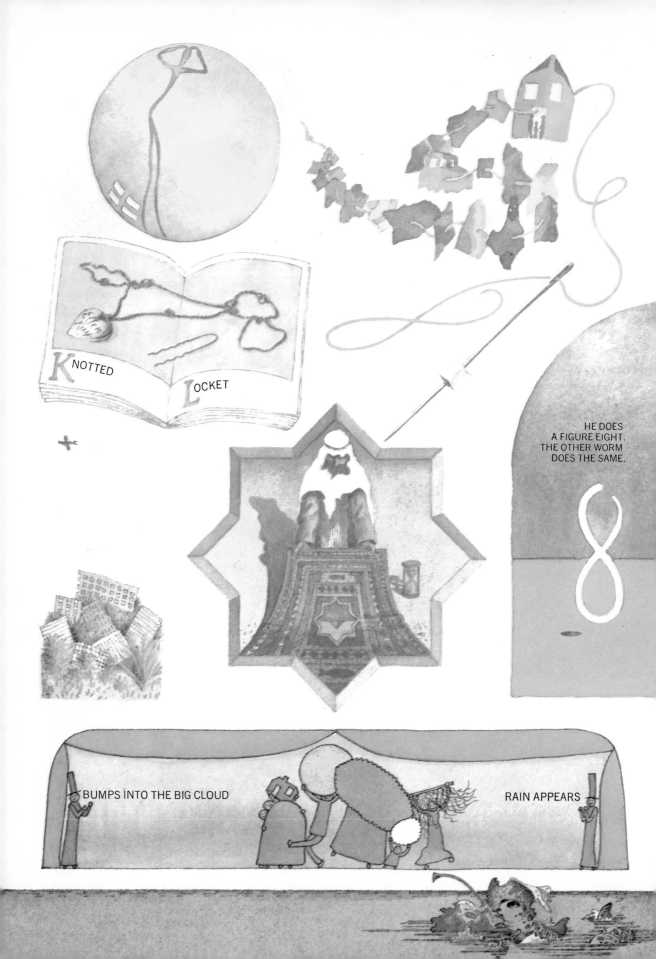

K NOTTED

L OCKET

HE DOES
A FIGURE EIGHT.
THE OTHER WORM
DOES THE SAME.

BUMPS INTO THE BIG CLOUD

RAIN APPEARS

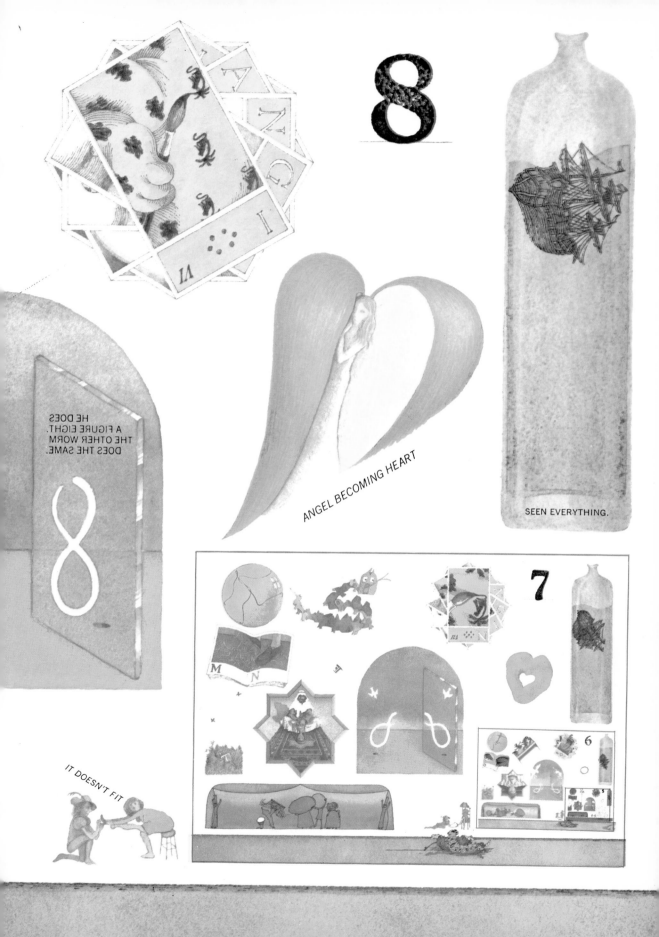

8

HE DOES
A FIGURE EIGHT.
THE OTHER WORM
DOES THE SAME.

ANGEL BECOMING HEART

SEEN EVERYTHING.

7

6

IT DOESN'T FIT

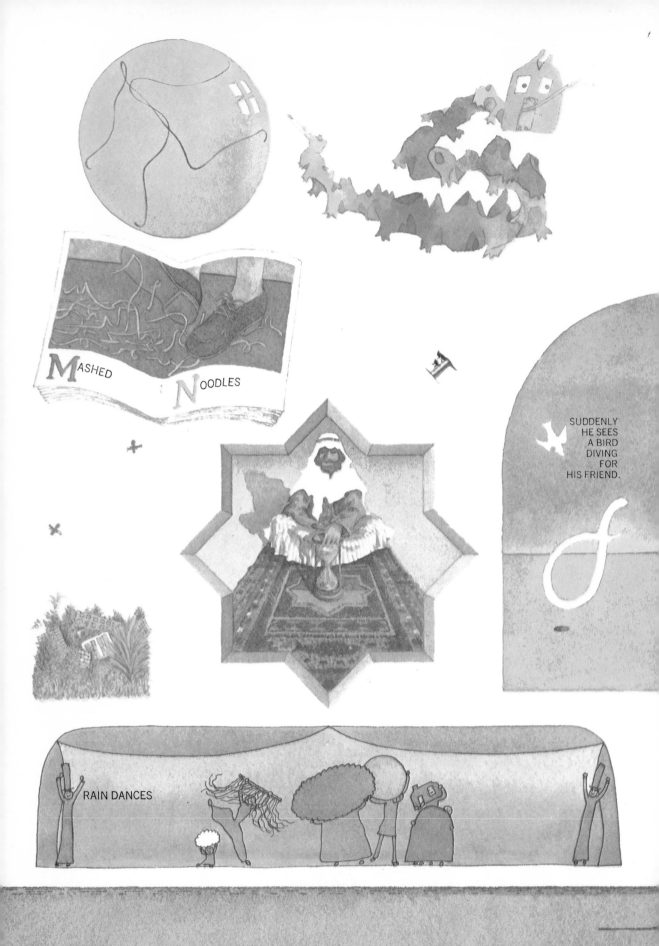

MASHED

NOODLES

SUDDENLY
HE SEES
A BIRD
DIVING
FOR
HIS FRIEND.

RAIN DANCES

7

SUDDENLY
HE SEES
A BIRD
DIVING
FOR
HIS FRIEND.

HEART BECOMING LIPS

BEEN IN MANY BATTLES
TOO!

IT DOESN'T FIT

6

5

OVERDONE

PIE

"HIDE!" HE CRIES, BUT HIS FRIEND DOESN'T MOVE.

EXCUSE ME

RAIN FALLS

PRODUCTION NOTE: MORE PLAYERS MAY BE ADDED HERE AS THUNDER, LIGHTNING, WIND, RAIN, SNOW, OR ADD ANYTHING ANYWHERE.

6

TOO MANY.

LIPS BECOMING RING

"HIDE!,"
HE CRIES,
BUT HIS
FRIEND
DOESN'T
MOVE.

IT DOESN'T FIT

5

4

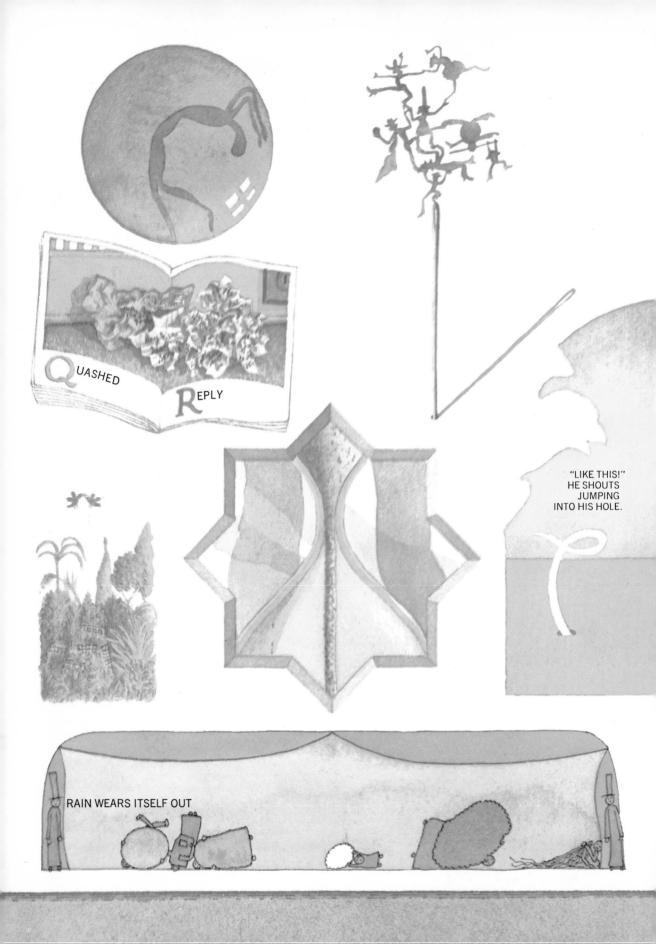

Q<small>UASHED</small>

R<small>EPLY</small>

"LIKE THIS!"
HE SHOUTS
JUMPING
INTO HIS HOLE.

RAIN WEARS ITSELF OUT

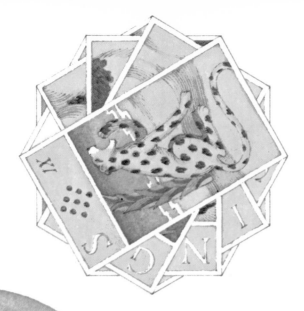

5

RING BECOMING LAMP

"LIKE THIS!"
HE SHOUTS
JUMPING
INTO HIS HOLE.

THAT'S WHY IT'S SINKING.

IT DOESN'T FIT

4

3

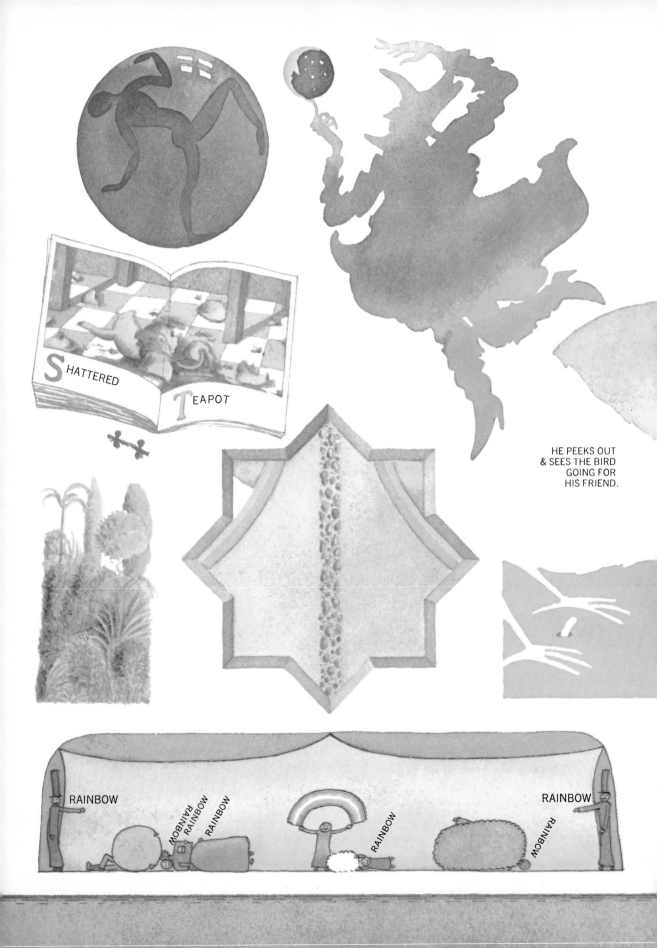

S HATTERED

T EAPOT

HE PEEKS OUT
& SEES THE BIRD
GOING FOR
HIS FRIEND.

RAINBOW

RAINBOW
RAINBOW
RAINBOW

RAINBOW

RAINBOW

RAINBOW

4

LAMP BECOMING ENVELOPE

AND ALTHOUGH IT HAS
BEEN AROUND THE WORLD,

3

IT DOESN'T FIT

2

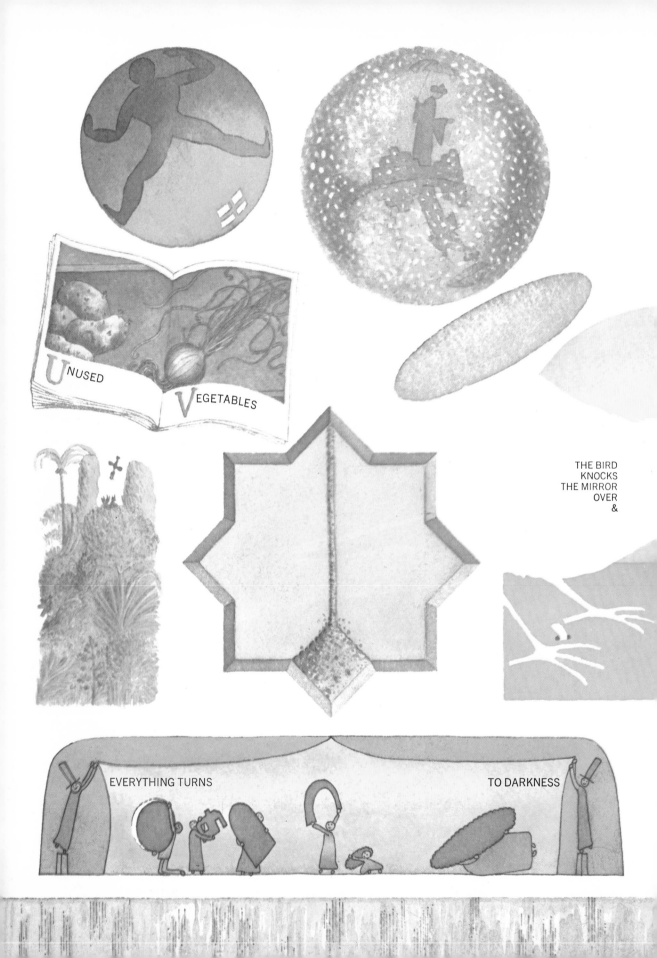

UNUSED

VEGETABLES

THE BIRD
KNOCKS
THE MIRROR
OVER
&

EVERYTHING TURNS   TO DARKNESS

3

ENVELOPE BECOMING HOUSE

IT'S GOING DOWN HAPPY.

2

1

IT DOESN'T FIT

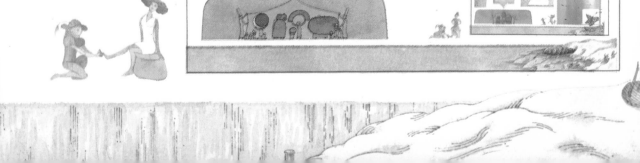

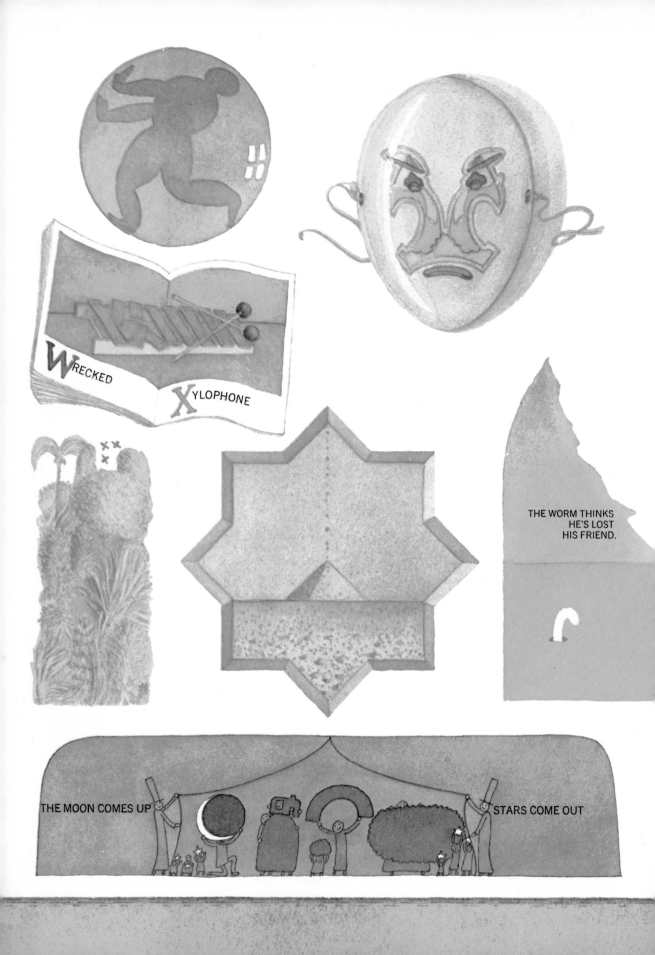

Wrecked Xylophone

THE WORM THINKS HE'S LOST HIS FRIEND.

THE MOON COMES UP

STARS COME OUT

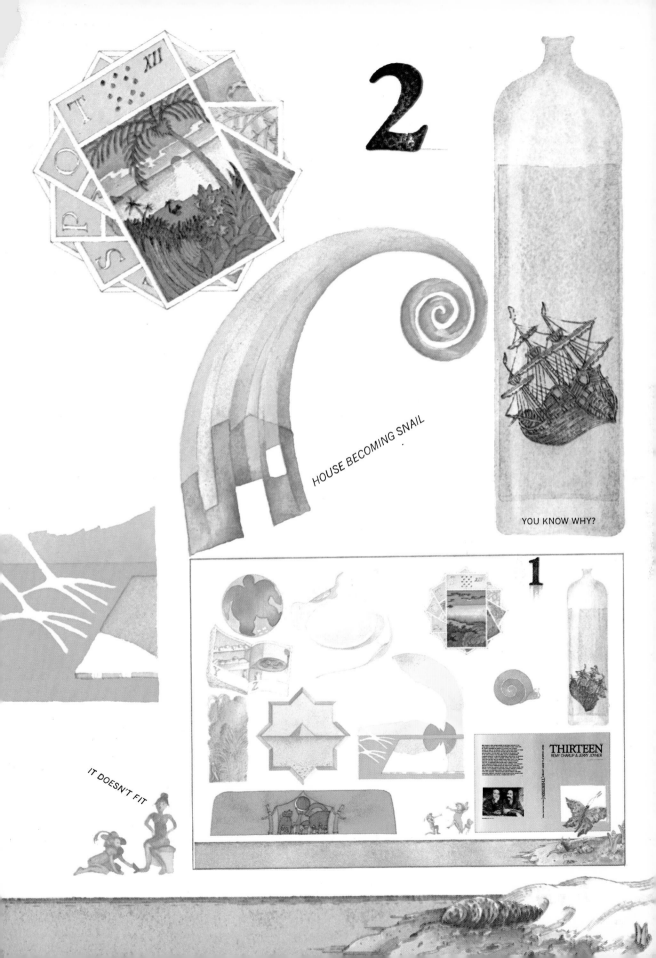

2

HOUSE BECOMING SNAIL

YOU KNOW WHY?

1

IT DOESN'T FIT

THIRTEEN
REMY CHARLIP & JERRY JOYNER

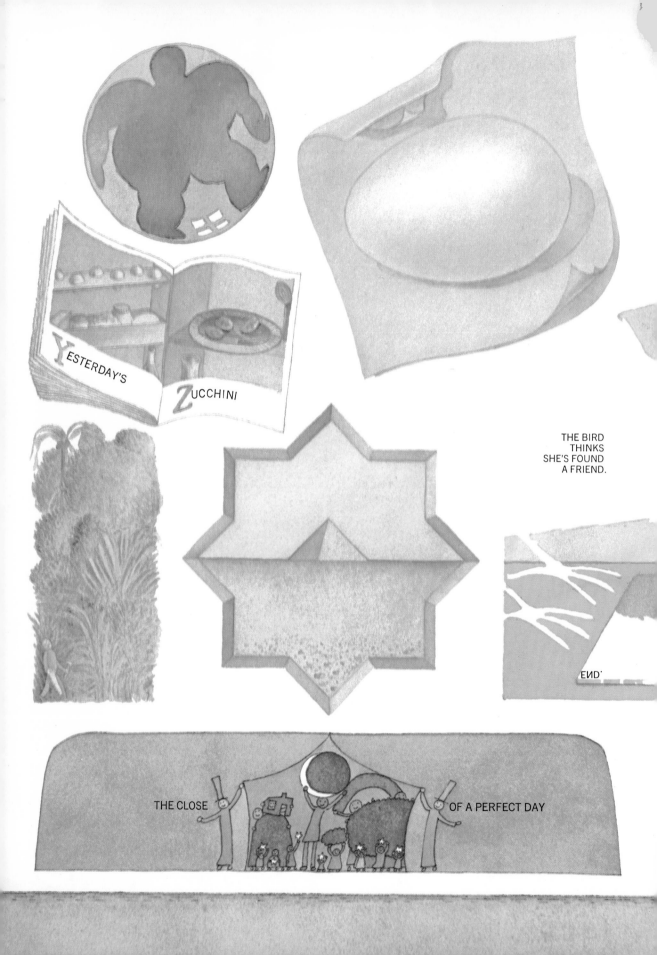

YESTERDAY'S

ZUCCHINI

THE BIRD
THINKS
SHE'S FOUND
A FRIEND.

END.

THE CLOSE   OF A PERFECT DAY

1

SNAIL BECOMING SWANS

IT HAS NEVER BEEN TO THE
BOTTOM OF THE SEA BEFORE.

IT FITS!

REMY CHARLIP & JERRY JOYNER SHARED THE WRITING & PAINTING OF THIS
UNIQUE BOOK IN UNUSUAL WAYS & IN MANY DIFFERENT PLACES. IN NEW YORK,
MR. CHARLIP DESCRIBED HIS CONCEPT OF THIRTEEN TO MR. JOYNER &
SHOWED HIM SOME OF THE ORIGINAL STORIES HE HAD ALREADY BEGUN. OF THESE
THE SINKING SHIP AND *THE GETTING THIN & GETTING FAT AGAIN DANCE*
WERE INCLUDED IN THE FINAL BOOK. THEY DECIDED TO COLLABORATE, AND
IN THE YEARS & TRAVELS THAT FOLLOWED, THEY MET & CORRESPONDED
& WORKED SEPARATELY & TOGETHER DISCOVERING & DEVELOPING THE INDIVIDUAL
STORIES & THE OVERALL FORM OF THE BOOK. IN PARIS, NINE YEARS AFTER
THEIR FIRST MEETING, THEY SAT OPPOSITE EACH OTHER TO PUT IT ALL TOGETHER,
CHOOSING, SKETCHING, ADDING, CUTTING, FITTING, PAINTING & WRITING.
TWELVE OF THE SEQUENCES WERE DECIDED UPON. IN GREECE, DURING
THREE SUBSEQUENT MONTHS, THEY DID THE FINAL PAINTINGS. THE THIRTEENTH
SEQUENCE EVOLVED BY IMPROVISATION. MR. CHARLIP & MR. JOYNER EACH
PAINTED AN IMAGE ON A SEPARATE PIECE OF PAPER. THEN TRADING PAPERS, THEY
PAINTED A VISUAL RESPONSE TO EACH OTHER'S IMAGES. WORKING ALTERNATELY
THEY PASSED THE PAPER BACK & FORTH. THE FINAL RESULT WAS THE
PAPER MAGIC SEQUENCE. *THIRTEEN* IS REMY CHARLIP'S TWENTY-THIRD BOOK
(*HARLEQUIN, HANDTALK, FORTUNATELY & ARM IN ARM*) & JERRY JOYNER'S THIRD
(*THE LOOKING BOOK & HOW FAR WILL A RUBBER BAND STRETCH?*).

PHOTOGRAPH BY KEN PATE

THIRTEEN
REMY CHARLIP & JERRY JOYNER

REMY CHARLIP & JERRY JOYNER **THIRTEEN** PARENTS MAGAZINE PRESS